Science
made easy

Key Stage 1
Ages 5-7 Workbook 2
Looking at Differences
and Similarities

Author
David Evans

LONDON • NEW YORK • SYDNEY • DELHI • PARIS • MUNICH • JOHANNESBURG

Alive or not alive?

Science facts

Living things can move, eat, grow and have babies. Things that are not alive do not do any of these things.

Science quiz

Draw a circle around each thing that is alive.

Science activity

Can you find five things around your home that are not alive?

2

Does it move?

Science facts

Living things can move by themselves. Some living things move quickly; others move slowly. Some living things run; others swim, fly, jump or crawl.

Science quiz

Draw a line joining each animal to the word describing how it moves.

slither

crawl

swim

fly

run

jump

Which of these animals can move the fastest?

....

Which of these animals can jump the highest?

....

Science activity

 Can you run faster than your friends? Have a race to see who can run the fastest.

Can you spot the living things?

Science facts

Animals are living things that can move from place to place by themselves. Animals are living things that eat food and grow bigger. Living things can produce babies.

Science quiz

Look carefully at this picture of a farm. Colour in all the things that are alive. Find three things that are not living. Draw a circle around each one.

Science activity

How many objects can you find in your home that come from things that were once living?

Does it have legs?

Science facts

Each part of your body does a different job. Your arms and hands help you to hold things. Your legs and feet help you to walk and run. Other animals have arms and legs, too. They use them in many different ways.

Science quiz

Draw a line joining each sentence to the animal it describes.

This animal moves without any arms or legs.

This animal has special arms to help it swim.

This animal uses its legs to catch food.

This animal has five arms.

This animal uses its arms and legs to climb trees.

Science activity

How many marbles can you pick up with one hand without dropping any? Can you pick up the same number with your other hand?

What is its body like?

Science facts

A human's body is covered with smooth skin. Different animals have different types of skin. Some animals have hair or fur; others have feathers. Some have scales or spines, and others have a hard shell.

Science quiz

Connect each animal to the type of skin it has.

Science activity

⚠ Fill a bowl with warm water (not hot). Try dipping in your elbows, fingers and toes. Which part of your skin is best for testing how warm the water is?

Do we all look the same?

Science facts

No two living things look exactly the same. Humans are different from one another in many ways. We can have different coloured hair and eyes. Our noses and ears can be different shapes. Our mouths and eyebrows may be shaped differently, too.

Science quiz

Can you spot six differences between these two girls? Put a cross (✗) by each difference.

Science activity

Can you touch your nose with your tongue? Can anyone else in your family do it? What about your friends?

Which kind of food is healthy?

Science facts

The foods that you eat are good for you in different ways. Meat, milk, eggs and fish all help you to grow. Bread, rice and potatoes give you energy to run and play. Vegetables and fruits help you to keep healthy.

Science quiz

Look at this meal, and draw a line joining each type of food to one of the circles below.

Food for growth

Food for energy

Food for health

Science activity

Keep a food diary for one week. Write down what you eat each day. Do you eat healthy food?

Will it make you better?

Science facts

When you are ill, a doctor may give you a bottle of medicine or pills to help you get better. These contain drugs that can stop illness. Cigarettes and alcoholic drinks contain drugs that are not good for you. They can make you ill.

Science quiz

Write the name of each drug under either **Helpful drugs** or **Harmful drugs**.

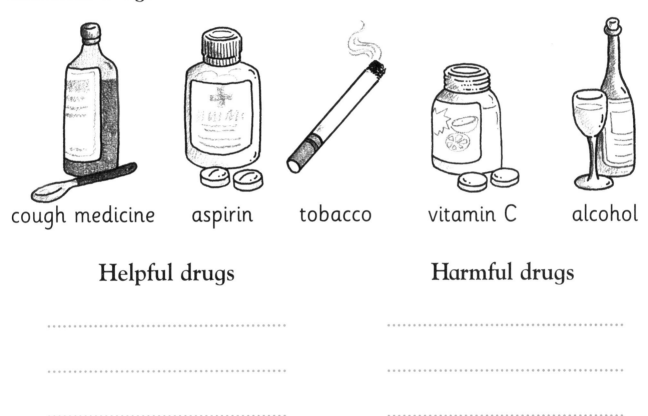

cough medicine   aspirin   tobacco   vitamin C   alcohol

Helpful drugs   **Harmful drugs**

....

....

....

Science activity

ⓘ With the help of an adult, can you find the names of any helpful drugs in your home? Are they tablets, capsules or liquids? Remember, even helpful drugs can be dangerous in the wrong amounts. Always ask an adult before you take any drugs.

Is it an adult or a child?

Science facts

All animals can make new living things: they reproduce themselves. It takes a male and a female animal to produce young. Young animals eat and grow into adult animals.

Science quiz

Draw lines to connect the male, female and young in each family.

Science activity

What kind of parents does a tadpole have? You may need to look for the answer in a book or on a computer.

Which sense is it?

Science facts

You have senses that tell you what is happening in the world around you. Your senses give you information about sounds, light, smells, tastes and what things feel like.

Science quiz

Different parts of the body sense different things. Choose words from the box below to describe what the boy and the dog in the picture are sensing. Label the parts using each word only once.

sound	light	smell	taste	touch

Science activity

⚠ Put one hand in ice-cold water and the other in hot water (make sure the water is not too hot). Leave your hands in the water for one minute. Then put both hands into warm water. Do they both feel the same?

Can it move in water?

Science facts

Animals live in many different places. They live on land, under the ground, in the air, in ponds and in the sea. Animals that live in water have special parts, such as fins and flat tails, to help them move.

Science quiz

Colour in the animals that live in water most of the time.

Science activity

How many fins does a goldfish have? Which parts of the fish help it move through water? If you do not have a goldfish, you may need to visit a pet shop or a pond.

What sort of animal is it?

Science facts
If you look closely at an animal, you can count how many legs it has. This helps to tell you what sort of animal it is.

Science quiz
Count how many legs each of these animals has, then find that number below and follow the wiggly line to find the animal's name.

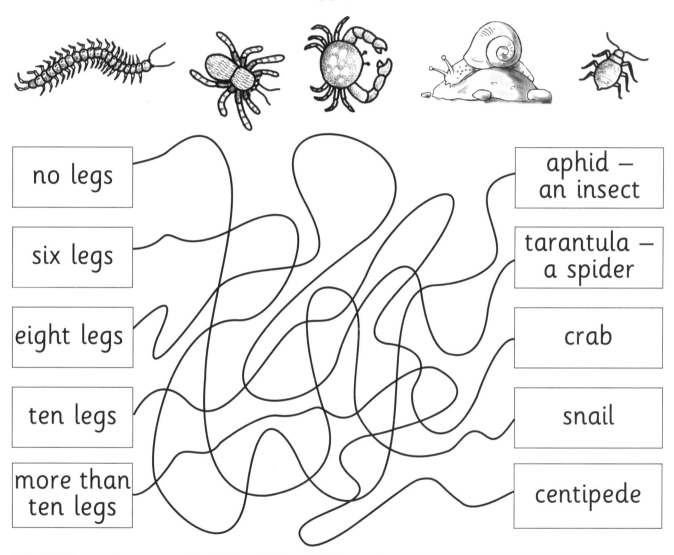

no legs

six legs

eight legs

ten legs

more than ten legs

aphid – an insect

tarantula – a spider

crab

snail

centipede

Science activity

(!) How many legs does a woodlouse have? See if you can find one, then use a soft paint brush to lift it into a see-through container so that you can count its legs. It may help to use a magnifying glass.

What sort of leaves does it have?

Science facts

Most plants have leaves. Many leaves are green. Different plants have different-shaped leaves. Plants use their leaves to make food, which helps them grow.

Science quiz

Colour all the leaves green. How are they different from each other? Follow the lines to find out the name of each leaf.

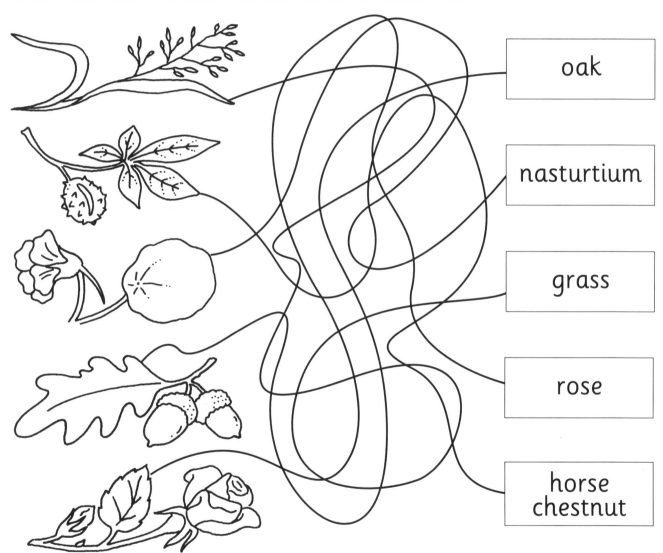

oak

nasturtium

grass

rose

horse chestnut

Science activity

(!) How many shades of green can you make using different-coloured paints? Which shades of green are like the leaves on plants near you?

Where are the seeds?

Science facts

Most of the plants you know have flowers. These flowers make seeds. There are many types of seed. You often find seeds inside fruits. When you plant seeds, they grow into new plants.

Science quiz

These fruits have been cut in half. Find the seeds, and colour them in.

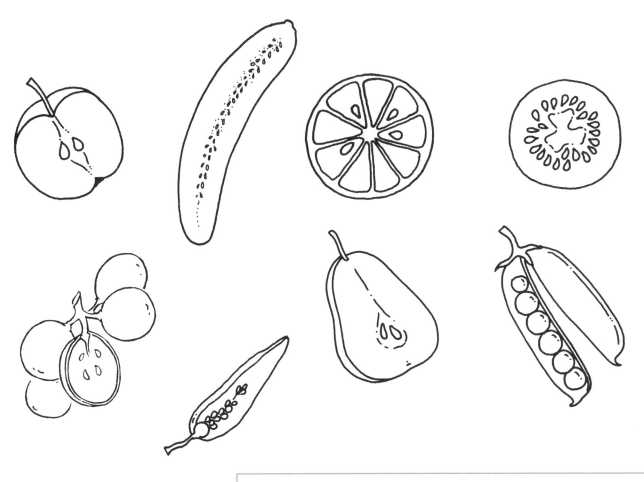

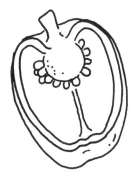

Science activity

Try growing sunflowers from seeds. Put some soil in a small plant pot, and bury the seeds just under the surface. Put the pot in a sunny place, and water the seeds a little every day. What happens?

Are all plants the same?

Science facts

There are many different types of plant. Trees have a woody trunk. They can grow very big, and their flowers can be difficult to see. Other plants are called shrubs. They have more than one trunk and often have bright flowers. Some plants are small with soft stems. They often have brightly coloured flowers; scientists call these plants herbs.

Science quiz

Which of the plants below are herbs, which are shrubs and which are trees? Draw a line from each plant to the correct name. What do all the plants have in common?

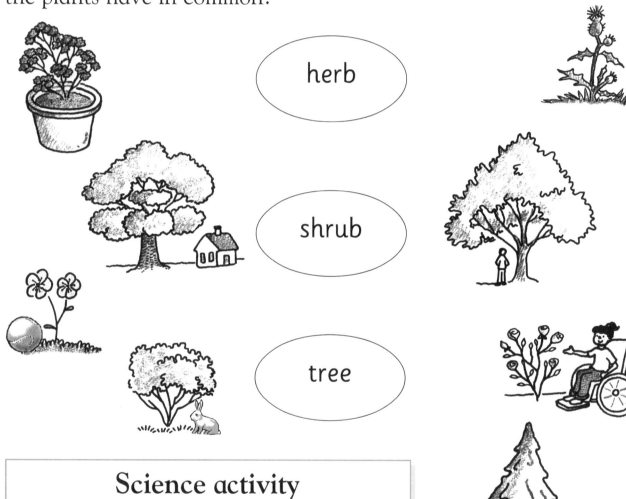

herb

shrub

tree

Science activity

Take a walk through a local park. Can you say which plants are herbs, which are shrubs, and which are trees?

Answer Section with Parents' Notes

Key Stage 1 Ages 5–7
Looking at differences and similarities

This section provides explanatory notes and answers to all the *Science quizzes*. Read through each page together, and ensure that your child understands each task. Point out any mistakes in your child's work, and correct any errors, but also remember to praise your child's efforts and achievements. Where appropriate, ask your child to predict the outcome of the *Science activities*. After each activity, challenge your child to explain his or her results.

When handling soil, make sure that gloves are worn and that hands are washed afterwards. Gloves are also advisable for freezer activities, as very cold objects can "burn" the skin.

---

2 ⭐

Alive or not alive?

Science facts
Living things can move, eat, grow and have babies. Things that are not alive do not do any of these things.

Science quiz
Draw a circle around each thing that is alive.

Science activity

Can you find five things around your home that are not alive?

This page introduces the concept of living things. Your child may identify something as being alive because it moves, and therefore may not realise that plants are also living things. Help your child by asking, "Is this alive or not alive?".

3

Does it move? ⭐

Science facts
Living things can move by themselves. Some living things move quickly; others move slowly. Some living things run; others swim, fly, jump or crawl.

Science quiz
Draw a line joining each animal to the word describing how it moves.

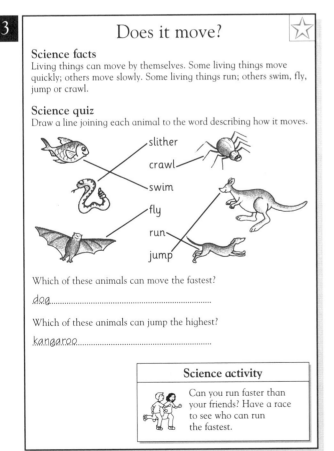

slither
crawl
swim
fly
run
jump

Which of these animals can move the fastest?

dog

Which of these animals can jump the highest?

kangaroo

Science activity

Can you run faster than your friends? Have a race to see who can run the fastest.

These activities show that living things move in different ways. Before the race, ask your child to predict who will be the best runner. Then encourage your child to use superlative words, such as *fastest* or *slowest*, to describe what happened.

---

4 ⭐

Can you spot the living things?

Science facts
Animals are living things that can move from place to place by themselves. Animals are living things that eat food and grow bigger. Living things can produce babies.

Science quiz

Look carefully at this picture of a farm. Colour in all the things that are alive. Find three things that are not living. Draw a circle around each one.

Science activity

How many objects can you find in your home that come from things that were once living?

Ask your child why he or she coloured particular things in the farm scene. Encourage comments such as, "The horse is eating." or "The tractor can't move by itself.". Your child may also realise that the trees and the grass are living things.

Does it have legs?

Science facts

Each part of your body does a different job. Your arms and hands help you to hold things. Your legs and feet help you to walk and run. Other animals have arms and legs, too. They use them in many different ways.

Science quiz

Draw a line joining each sentence to the animal it describes.

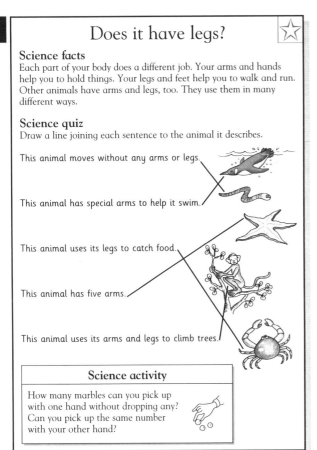

This animal moves without any arms or legs.

This animal has special arms to help it swim.

This animal uses its legs to catch food.

This animal has five arms.

This animal uses its arms and legs to climb trees.

Science activity

How many marbles can you pick up with one hand without dropping any? Can you pick up the same number with your other hand?

These activities show that human and animal bodies are made of different parts, each with specific functions. Let your child try the experiment several times to improve his or her score, and remember to praise your child's efforts.

What is its body like?

Science facts

A human's body is covered with smooth skin. Different animals have different types of skin. Some animals have hair or fur; others have feathers. Some have scales or spines, and others have a hard shell.

Science quiz

Connect each animal to the type of skin it has.

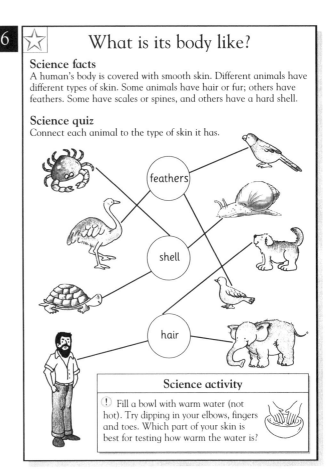

feathers

shell

hair

Science activity

(!) Fill a bowl with warm water (not hot). Try dipping in your elbows, fingers and toes. Which part of your skin is best for testing how warm the water is?

Here, your child learns that different animals have different body coverings. Be sure to supervise the experiment. Ask your child to predict which part of the body will be the most sensitive to heat. He or she could try elbows, fingers, toes, hands and knees.

Do we all look the same?

Science facts

No two living things look exactly the same. Humans are different from one another in many ways. We can have different coloured hair and eyes. Our noses and ears can be different shapes. Our mouths and eyebrows may be shaped differently, too.

Science quiz

Can you spot six differences between these two girls? Put a cross (✗) by each difference.

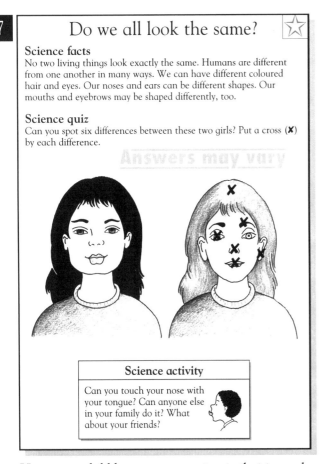

Answers may vary

Science activity

Can you touch your nose with your tongue? Can anyone else in your family do it? What about your friends?

Here, your child learns to recognise similarities and differences between people. Discourage him or her from describing one person's look as better than another. The ability to touch the nose with the tongue is inherited. Ask your child to try it.

Which kind of food is healthy?

Science facts

The foods that you eat are good for you in different ways. Meat, milk, eggs and fish all help you to grow. Bread, rice and potatoes give you energy to run and play. Vegetables and fruits help you to keep healthy.

Science quiz

Look at this meal, and draw a line joining each type of food to one of the circles below.

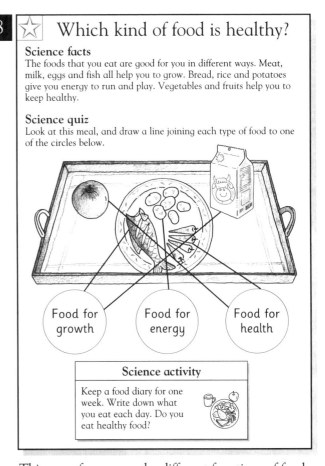

Food for growth

Food for energy

Food for health

Science activity

Keep a food diary for one week. Write down what you eat each day. Do you eat healthy food?

This page focuses on the different functions of food. Talk about the food your child eats, and identify which elements help growth, give energy, or provide minerals and vitamins for health. You may wish to introduce the terms *protein*, *fat* and *carbohydrate*.

Will it make you better?

Science facts

When you are ill, a doctor may give you a bottle of medicine or pills to help you get better. These contain drugs that can stop illness. Cigarettes and alcoholic drinks contain drugs that are not good for you. They can make you ill.

Science quiz

Write the name of each drug under either **Helpful drugs** or **Harmful drugs**.

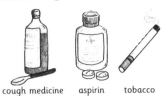

cough medicine   aspirin   tobacco   vitamin C   alcohol

Helpful drugs	**Harmful drugs**
cough medicine	tobacco
aspirin	alcohol
vitamin C	

Science activity

(!) With the help of an adult, can you find the names of any helpful drugs in your home? Are they tablets, capsules or liquids? Remember, even helpful drugs can be dangerous in the wrong amounts. Always ask an adult before you take any drugs.

It is never too early to tell your child that some drugs are harmful and to inform him or her about the dangers of smoking tobacco and drinking alcohol. The experiment must be carried out under strict adult supervision.

Is it an adult or a child?

Science facts

All animals can make new living things: they reproduce themselves. It takes a male and a female animal to produce young. Young animals eat and grow into adult animals.

Science quiz

Draw lines to connect the male, female and young in each family.

Science activity

What kind of parents does a tadpole have? You may need to look for the answer in a book or on a computer.

Here, your child learns that humans and other animals produce offspring, which grow into adults. Encourage your child to use the words *birth*, *male*, *female*, *adult* and *offspring*. Use a reference book or CD-ROM to study frogs.

Which sense is it?

Science facts

You have senses that tell you what is happening in the world around you. Your senses give you information about sounds, light, smells, tastes and what things feel like.

Science quiz

Different parts of the body sense different things. Choose words from the box below to describe what the boy and the dog in the picture are sensing. Label the parts using each word only once.

sound	light	smell	taste	touch

sound   light
taste
smell
touch

Science activity

(!) Put one hand in ice-cold water and the other in hot water (make sure the water is not too hot). Leave your hands in the water for one minute. Then put both hands into warm water. Do they both feel the same?

The five senses (taste, smell, touch, hearing and sight) are well known. You may wish to discuss other senses, such as pain, movement and heaviness. You need to supervise the experiment. Ensure that the water is not too hot.

Can it move in water?

Science facts

Animals live in many different places. They live on land, under the ground, in the air, in ponds and in the sea. Animals that live in water have special parts, such as fins and flat tails, to help them move.

Science quiz

Colour in the animals that live in water most of the time.

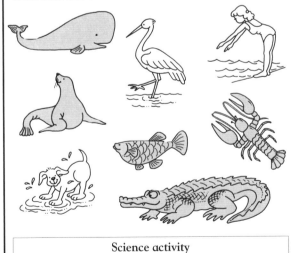

Science activity

(!) How many fins does a goldfish have? Which parts of the fish help it move through water? If you do not have a goldfish, you may need to visit a pet shop or a pond.

This page looks at animals that are specially adapted to live in water. Encourage your child to observe the goldfish closely. Can he or she work out what the various fins are used for? Ask your child if the fish is a living thing, and why.

13 · What sort of animal is it?

Science facts
If you look closely at an animal, you can count how many legs it has. This helps to tell you what sort of animal it is.

Science quiz
Count how many legs each of these animals has, then find that number below and follow the wiggly line to find the animal's name.

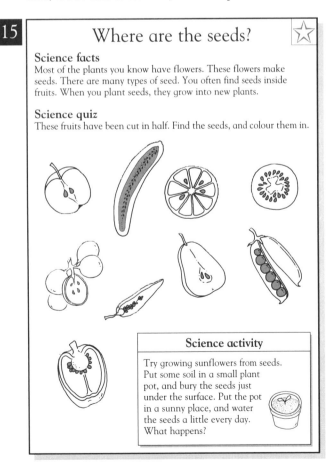

no legs

six legs

eight legs

ten legs

more than ten legs

aphid – an insect

tarantula – a spider

crab

snail

centipede

Science activity
(!) How many legs does a woodlouse have? See if you can find one, then use a soft paint brush to lift it into a see-through container so that you can count its legs. It may help to use a magnifying glass.

These exercises teach your child to use observational skills to classify living things. You could extend the quiz activity by asking your child to suggest animals with two, four and five legs – a bird, a cat and a starfish, for example.

14 · What sort of leaves does it have?

Science facts
Most plants have leaves. Many leaves are green. Different plants have different-shaped leaves. Plants use their leaves to make food, which helps them grow.

Science quiz
Colour all the leaves green. How are they different from each other? Follow the lines to find out the name of each leaf.

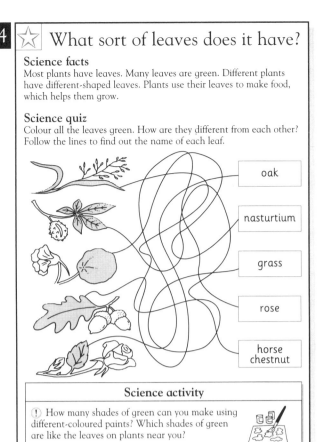

oak

nasturtium

grass

rose

horse chestnut

Science activity
(!) How many shades of green can you make using different-coloured paints? Which shades of green are like the leaves on plants near you?

Here, your child learns that different plants have different leaves. Talk to your child about the shapes and colours of leaves. You could keep the colours mixed during the experiment and use them to match against the plants in a garden or park.

15 · Where are the seeds?

Science facts
Most of the plants you know have flowers. These flowers make seeds. There are many types of seed. You often find seeds inside fruits. When you plant seeds, they grow into new plants.

Science quiz
These fruits have been cut in half. Find the seeds, and colour them in.

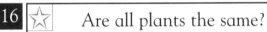

Science activity
Try growing sunflowers from seeds. Put some soil in a small plant pot, and bury the seeds just under the surface. Put the pot in a sunny place, and water the seeds a little every day. What happens?

The theme of this page is seeds. In the experiment, first ask your child to suggest how the seeds could be germinated and grown. Use a commercially packaged soil for safety. You could extend the experiment by growing different kinds of seeds.

16 · Are all plants the same?

Science facts
There are many different types of plant. Trees have a woody trunk. They can grow very big, and their flowers can be difficult to see. Other plants are called shrubs. They have more than one trunk and often have bright flowers. Some plants are small with soft stems. They often have brightly coloured flowers; scientists call these plants herbs.

Science quiz
Which of the plants below are herbs, which are shrubs and which are trees? Draw a line from each plant to the correct name. What do all the plants have in common?

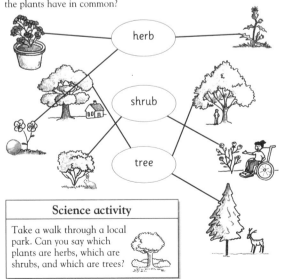

herb

shrub

tree

Science activity
Take a walk through a local park. Can you say which plants are herbs, which are shrubs, and which are trees?

This page requires your child to look carefully at the features of plants and to decide whether they are herbs, shrubs or trees. In the experiment, ask, "Why have you said that?" to see whether your child has understood the criteria for classification.

Is it metal, wood or plastic?

Science facts

The things around you are made from different materials, such as metal, wood and plastic. Metals often look shiny. They feel cold, and they go "ching" when you tap them. Wood feels warm. It is not shiny, and it makes a hollow "thud" when you tap it. Plastics are often smooth and shiny. They feel warm, and they usually make a dull "clunk" when you tap them.

Science quiz

Help Alfie decide if these objects are made of metal, wood or plastic. First write the words **metal**, **wood** and **plastic** on the dotted lines. Then draw a line joining each object to the correct word.

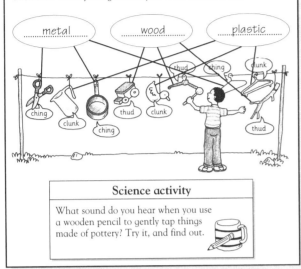

metal   wood   plastic

Science activity

What sound do you hear when you use a wooden pencil to gently tap things made of pottery? Try it, and find out.

This page shows that materials can be grouped by features we see, hear and feel. Encourage your child to predict what he or she might hear in the experiment, and then to describe the actual sound. Compare the noises made by pottery and metal.

Is it rough or smooth?

Science facts

Some surfaces are smooth. Your hand can slide easily over them. Some surfaces feel rough. They are difficult to rub. Very rough surfaces can hurt your hand if you rub them.

Science quiz

Which of these surfaces is the roughest? Which is the smoothest? Can you list these things in order of roughness? Write the roughest one first.

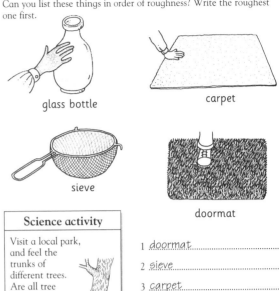

glass bottle   carpet

sieve

doormat

Science activity

Visit a local park, and feel the trunks of different trees. Are all tree trunks rough?

1 doormat
2 sieve
3 carpet
4 glass bottle

Here, your child uses his or her hands to judge the roughness of surfaces. Extend the experiment by making a "rubbing" of the tree bark with a wax crayon and a sheet of paper. The more even the colour, the smoother the surface of the bark.

Is it shiny?

Science facts

Metals are often shiny. If the surface of a metal is polished, you can see your reflection when you look at it. This is why metals are used to make mirrors. If you shine a torch onto a shiny metal surface, you can see a reflection of the light on the wall.

Science quiz

Which of these spoons is made of metal? Tick (✔) the correct box.

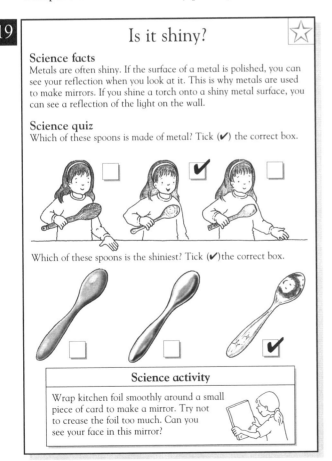

Which of these spoons is the shiniest? Tick (✔) the correct box.

Science activity

Wrap kitchen foil smoothly around a small piece of card to make a mirror. Try not to crease the foil too much. Can you see your face in this mirror?

These activities teach your child that metals are shiny and that some metals are shinier than others. As an additional activity, ask your child to polish some tarnished coins to see what happens and then to decide which coin is the shiniest.

Will it be pulled by a magnet?

Science facts

Magnets are made of iron. They can attract some types of metal but not all. Some magnets are stronger than others. They pull metals towards themselves more strongly.

Science quiz

Katie is holding a magnet over a tray of paper clips. The rounded paper clips are made of metal, and the triangular clips are made of plastic. Colour in the paper clips that will be attracted to the magnet.

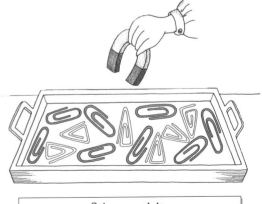

Science activity

Can you find five things in your home that are attracted to a magnet? Use a refrigerator magnet to find out. Write a list of things that are attracted to the magnet, and write another list of things that are not attracted to it.

You will need a fridge magnet or a magnet from a toy shop for the activities on this page. Your child may be confused by "metallic" plastics, which are not attracted to the magnet. Explain that the material is plastic but is made to look like metal.

Is it a rock?

Science facts
Mountains, hills, cliffs, stones and pebbles are made of rock. Jewels are made of rock. Garden soil and sand are made up of many tiny bits of rock. There are many different types of rock. Some rocks are very hard, others are soft.

Science quiz
Colour all the different rocks you can see in this picture.

Science activity
Start a rock collection. But remember to ask an adult before you take any rocks from a beach or park. Are all your rocks the same colour?

Here, your child learns that there are different types of rock. You could visit a beach to find a variety of pebbles, and a jeweller's shop to see gem stones. Encourage your child to start a rock collection and to sort the rocks by colour.

Does it change forever?

Science facts
When you leave water in a freezer, it changes into ice: it changes from a liquid to a solid. When you take the ice out of the freezer, it changes back into water. When you cook an egg, it changes from being runny to being solid, but no matter what you do, you cannot change the solid egg back into the runny egg.

Science quiz
Look at this kitchen. Draw a circle around each food item that changes when you heat it and then changes back again when it cools down. Put a (✗) cross over each food item that changes when you heat it but does not change back when it cools down.

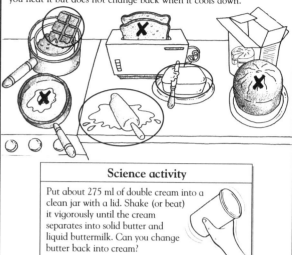

Science activity
Put about 275 ml of double cream into a clean jar with a lid. Shake (or beat) it vigorously until the cream separates into solid butter and liquid buttermilk. Can you change butter back into cream?

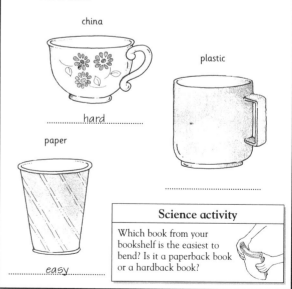

This page looks at how materials change when they are heated or cooled. The important point for your child to learn is that some changes are reversible (ice that melts can be refrozen) and some are irreversible (a cake cannot be unbaked).

What stretches the most?

Science facts
Some materials stretch a lot when you pull them. Other materials are hard to stretch.

Science quiz
Rachel tested pieces of different materials to see how much they stretched. Each piece of material was the same length. She used the same piece of heavy metal to give each material the same amount of pull. She then measured how much each one had stretched. Here are her results. Write **1** in the box under the strip that stretched to the longest length; write **2** under the strip that stretched to the next longest length; and so on.

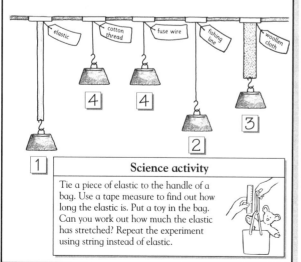

Science activity
Tie a piece of elastic to the handle of a bag. Use a tape measure to find out how long the elastic is. Put a toy in the bag. Can you work out how much the elastic has stretched? Repeat the experiment using string instead of elastic.

On this page, your child learns that some materials stretch more than others. Encourage your child to predict the results of the experiment before carrying it out.

What bends the most?

Science facts
Some things, such as plastic carrier bags, bend easily. Other things, such as dinner plates, do not bend at all. The more you pull or push some things, the more they bend.

Science quiz
Jack is gently squeezing some cups to find out which material is the easiest to bend. Can you write **easy** below the cup that Jack will find the easiest to bend? Write **hard** below the cup that he will find the hardest to bend.

china

plastic

.... hard ....

paper

....

Science activity
Which book from your bookshelf is the easiest to bend? Is it a paperback book or a hardback book?

.... *easy* ....

On this page, your child learns that some materials bend when a force is applied. Ask your child to predict which books will bend easily. You could extend this activity by bending supple materials, such as modelling clay and dough.

25 — What cools the quickest?

Science facts
When things are heated, they become hot. When the heat is taken away, they cool down. Some things cool quickly, others cool more slowly.

Science quiz
Oliver baked some scones in a very hot oven at 180°C. He took them out of the oven and left them to cool. After ten minutes, he stuck a thermometer inside each scone. Tick (✔) the box by the scone that cooled the quickest.

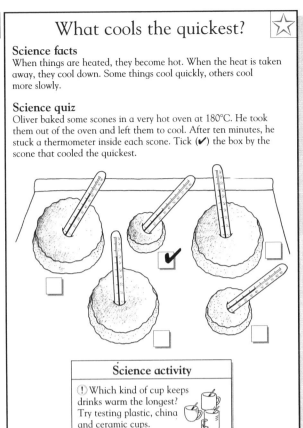

Science activity
(!) Which kind of cup keeps drinks warm the longest? Try testing plastic, china and ceramic cups.

Here, your child learns that some things cool quicker than others. You will need to supervise the experiment closely. Emphasise that to make the test fair, the cups must contain the same amount of liquid and stand in the same place.

26 — Can you make a circuit?

Science facts
To make a bulb light up, it must be in a complete electrical circuit. Buzzers and motors also need to be in a complete circuit to work. If there is a break in the circuit, these things will not work.

Science quiz
Jessica wants to make a circuit to make a motor turn. She then wants to make another circuit to make a buzzer buzz. She also wants to make a circuit to light up a bulb.

Draw in the motor to complete this circuit.

Draw in the buzzer to complete this circuit.

Draw in the bulb to complete this circuit.

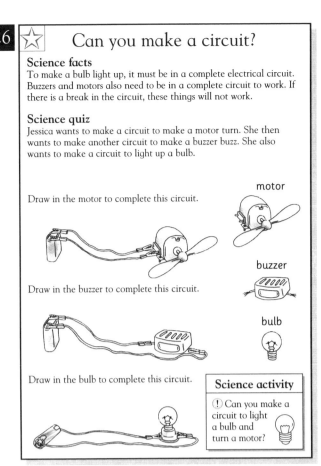

motor

buzzer

bulb

Science activity
(!) Can you make a circuit to light a bulb and turn a motor?

These activities show that before a device such as a bulb or buzzer can work, the components must be in the correct order and connected to form a complete circuit. By doing the activity, your child will discover this principle for him- or herself.

27 — Which one moves the fastest?

Science facts
A push is a force. A pull is also a force. Forces can make things move. Forces can make some things move fast. They make some things move faster than others.

Science quiz
Phoebe is playing with a ball. Colour in the pictures where she is making the ball move fast.

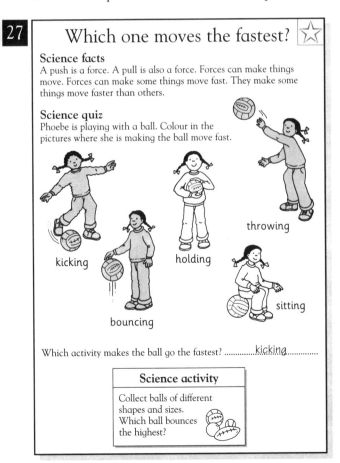

throwing

kicking

holding

bouncing

sitting

Which activity makes the ball go the fastest? ....kicking..........

Science activity
Collect balls of different shapes and sizes. Which ball bounces the highest?

This page introduces the idea that forces can make objects move. Help your child to decide how to measure the height of the bounce (for example, with a tape measure or a chalk mark on a wall) and to keep a record of the results.

28 — Will it change direction?

Science facts
Pushes and pulls are forces that make things move. Blowing is a force that pushes air to make things move. Blowing against a moving thing can make it stop. Blowing can also make moving things change direction.

Science quiz
Daisy is using a straw to blow at a table-tennis ball. Which picture shows her blowing in a way that will make the ball change direction? Circle A or B.

A

B

Science activity
Ask someone to roll or throw a ball towards you. How can you make it change direction? Try different ways.

On this page, your child discovers that a force can change the direction in which an object moves. Explain that blowing, sucking, kicking, throwing and hitting are all forces. If your child is asthmatic, avoid blowing experiments.

Which light is the brightest?

Science facts
The Sun is a very bright source of light. You must never look directly at the Sun because the bright light can damage your eyes. Light also comes from other sources, which are not so bright. Candles, torches, room lights and table lamps all give out light.

Science quiz
Which of these candles gives the brightest light? Write **1** in the box by the brightest light; write **2** in the box by the next brightest; and write **3** in the box by the least bright light.

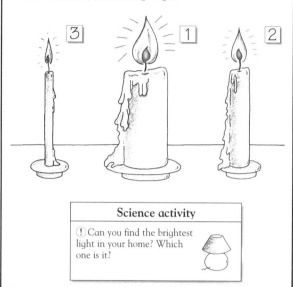

Science activity
(!) Can you find the brightest light in your home? Which one is it?

This page looks at sources of light. Encourage your child to use the words *bright*, *brighter* and *brightest*. To judge brightness, use each light to cast the shadow of an object on a piece of paper. The clearer the shadow, the brighter the light.

What makes a shadow?

Science facts
When you shine a torch at a wall, the wall seems brighter. If you put your hand over the torch, it blocks all the light, and the wall stays dark. If you hold your hand between the torch and the wall, you make a shadow. The closer your hand is to the torch, the bigger the shadow.

Science quiz
Which of these children will make the largest shadow? Circle that child's name.

Jo · (Kate) · Tom · Ben

Science activity
Use a torch and your hands to make a shadow that looks like a bird. Can you make a shadow that looks like a dog?

The theme of this page is shadows. For the quiz, point out that Kate's hand is closer to the torch than Tom's. For the experiment, use a powerful torch or a slide projector. You may need to show your child how to make shadow animals.

How do you make that sound?

Science facts
You can make sounds when you beat, shake or scrape things. You can make sounds when you pluck strings or use a bow. Blowing through a hole can also make a sound.

Science quiz
Draw a circle around each instrument that makes a sound when you beat it.

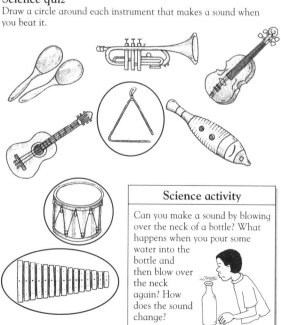

Science activity
Can you make a sound by blowing over the neck of a bottle? What happens when you pour some water into the bottle and then blow over the neck again? How does the sound change?

These activities show that sounds are made in different ways. You will need to show your child how to blow over the neck of a bottle. If your child is asthmatic or finds this activity too difficult, beat the bottle with a spoon instead.

What makes the loudest sound?

Science facts
You use your ears to hear sounds. Some sounds are loud and easy to hear. Other sounds are quiet and hard to hear. Some sounds are so loud they hurt your ears. People can wear ear protectors to protect their hearing in places where sounds are very loud.

Science quiz
If you stood next to each of these things, which one would sound the loudest? Put a tick (✔) in the box beside it. Which one would sound the quietest? Put a cross (✘) in the box beside it. Circle the one that is so loud you would need to wear ear protectors to stand near it?

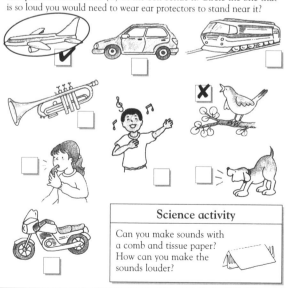

Science activity
Can you make sounds with a comb and tissue paper? How can you make the sounds louder?

Here, your child learns that the loudness of sounds can vary. Encourage your child to use the words *loud*, *louder* and *loudest*. The activity with the comb and paper is good because your child's lips will feel the vibrations that make the sound.

Is it metal, wood or plastic?

Science facts

The things around you are made from different materials, such as metal, wood and plastic. Metals often look shiny. They feel cold, and they go "ching" when you tap them. Wood feels warm. It is not shiny, and it makes a hollow "thud" when you tap it. Plastics are often smooth and shiny. They feel warm, and they usually make a dull "clunk" when you tap them.

Science quiz

Help Alfie decide if these objects are made of metal, wood or plastic. First write the words **metal**, **wood** and **plastic** on the dotted lines. Then draw a line joining each object to the correct word.

Science activity

What sound do you hear when you use a wooden pencil to gently tap things made of pottery? Try it, and find out.

Is it rough or smooth?

Science facts

Some surfaces are smooth. Your hand can slide easily over them. Some surfaces feel rough. They are difficult to rub. Very rough surfaces can hurt your hand if you rub them.

Science quiz

Which of these surfaces is the roughest? Which is the smoothest? Can you list these things in order of roughness? Write the roughest one first.

glass bottle

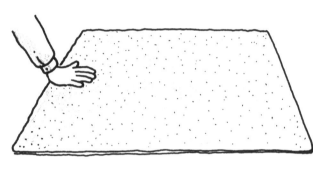

carpet

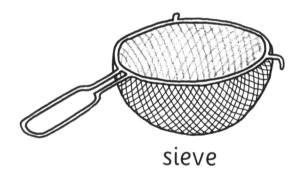

sieve

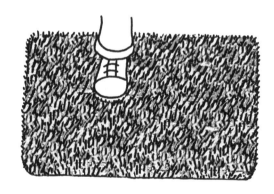

doormat

Science activity

Visit a local park, and feel the trunks of different trees. Are all tree trunks rough?

1 ....

2 ....

3 ....

4 ....

18

Is it shiny?

Science facts

Metals are often shiny. If the surface of a metal is polished, you can see your reflection when you look at it. This is why metals are used to make mirrors. If you shine a torch onto a shiny metal surface, you can see a reflection of the light on the wall.

Science quiz

Which of these spoons is made of metal? Tick (✔) the correct box.

Which of these spoons is the shiniest? Tick (✔) the correct box.

Science activity

Wrap kitchen foil smoothly around a small piece of card to make a mirror. Try not to crease the foil too much. Can you see your face in this mirror?

Will it be pulled by a magnet?

Science facts

Magnets are made of iron. They can attract some types of metal but not all. Some magnets are stronger than others. They pull metals towards themselves more strongly.

Science quiz

Katie is holding a magnet over a tray of paper clips. The rounded paper clips are made of metal, and the triangular clips are made of plastic. Colour in the paper clips that will be attracted to the magnet.

Science activity

Can you find five things in your home that are attracted to a magnet? Use a refrigerator magnet to find out. Write a list of things that are attracted to the magnet, and write another list of things that are not attracted to it.

Is it a rock?

Science facts

Mountains, hills, cliffs, stones and pebbles are made of rock. Jewels are made of rock. Garden soil and sand are made up of many tiny bits of rock. There are many different types of rock. Some rocks are very hard, others are soft.

Science quiz

Colour all the different rocks you can see in this picture.

Science activity

Start a rock collection. But remember to ask an adult before you take any rocks from a beach or park. Are all your rocks the same colour?

Does it change forever?

Science facts

When you leave water in a freezer, it changes into ice: it changes from a liquid to a solid. When you take the ice out of the freezer, it changes back into water. When you cook an egg, it changes from being runny to being solid, but no matter what you do, you cannot change the solid egg back into the runny egg.

Science quiz

Look at this kitchen. Draw a circle around each food item that changes when you heat it and then changes back again when it cools down. Put a (✘) cross over each food item that changes when you heat it but does not change back when it cools down.

Science activity

Put about 275 ml of double cream into a clean jar with a lid. Shake (or beat) it vigorously until the cream separates into solid butter and liquid buttermilk. Can you change butter back into cream?

Science facts

Some materials stretch a lot when you pull them. Other materials are hard to stretch.

Science quiz

Rachel tested pieces of different materials to see how much they stretched. Each piece of material was the same length. She used the same piece of heavy metal to give each material the same amount of pull. She then measured how much each one had stretched. Here are her results. Write **1** in the box under the strip that stretched to the longest length; write **2** under the strip that stretched to the next longest length; and so on.

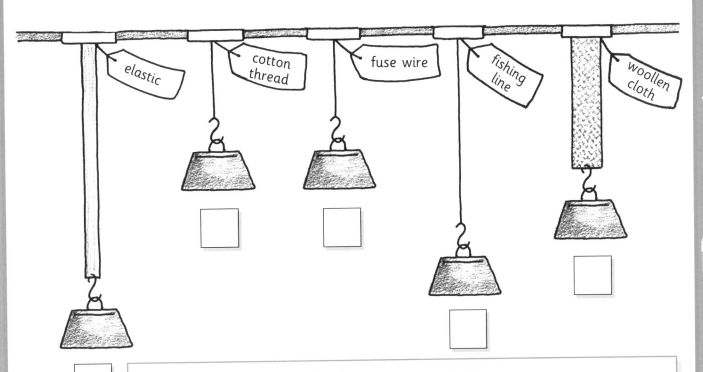

Science activity

Tie a piece of elastic to the handle of a bag. Use a tape measure to find out how long the elastic is. Put a toy in the bag. Can you work out how much the elastic has stretched? Repeat the experiment using string instead of elastic.

What bends the most?

Science facts

Some things, such as plastic carrier bags, bend easily. Other things, such as dinner plates, do not bend at all. The more you pull or push some things, the more they bend.

Science quiz

Jack is gently squeezing some cups to find out which material is the easiest to bend. Can you write **easy** below the cup that Jack will find the easiest to bend? Write **hard** below the cup that he will find the hardest to bend.

china

....

plastic

paper

....

Science activity

Which book from your bookshelf is the easiest to bend? Is it a paperback book or a hardback book?

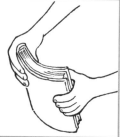

What cools the quickest?

Science facts
When things are heated, they become hot. When the heat is taken away, they cool down. Some things cool quickly, others cool more slowly.

Science quiz
Oliver baked some scones in a very hot oven at 180°C. He took them out of the oven and left them to cool. After ten minutes, he stuck a thermometer inside each scone. Tick (✔) the box by the scone that cooled the quickest.

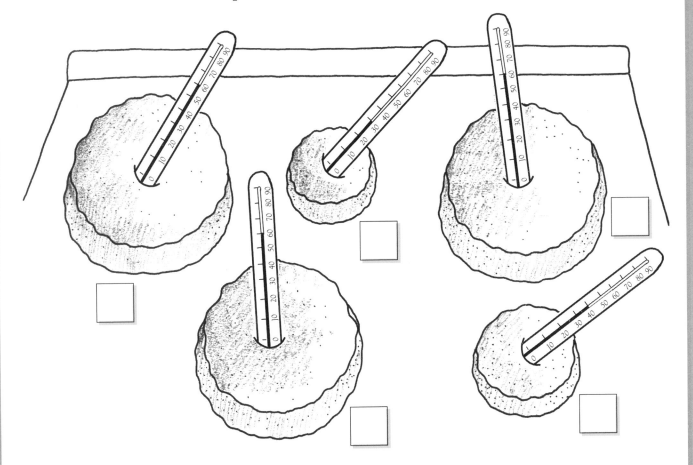

Science activity

(!) Which kind of cup keeps drinks warm the longest? Try testing plastic, china and ceramic cups.

Can you make a circuit?

Science facts

To make a bulb light up, it must be in a complete electrical circuit. Buzzers and motors also need to be in a complete circuit to work. If there is a break in the circuit, these things will not work.

Science quiz

Jessica wants to make a circuit to make a motor turn. She then wants to make another circuit to make a buzzer buzz. She also wants to make a circuit to light up a bulb.

Draw in the motor to complete this circuit.

motor

Draw in the buzzer to complete this circuit.

buzzer

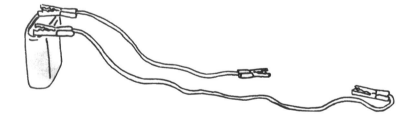

Draw in the bulb to complete this circuit.

bulb

Science activity

⚠ Can you make a circuit to light a bulb and turn a motor?

26

Which one moves the fastest?

Science facts

A push is a force. A pull is also a force. Forces can make things move. Forces can make some things move fast. They make some things move faster than others.

Science quiz

Phoebe is playing with a ball. Colour in the pictures where she is making the ball move fast.

throwing

kicking

bouncing

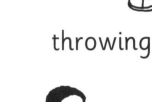

holding

sitting

Which activity makes the ball go the fastest? ....

Science activity

Collect balls of different shapes and sizes. Which ball bounces the highest?

Will it change direction?

Science facts

Pushes and pulls are forces that make things move. Blowing is a force that pushes air to make things move. Blowing against a moving thing can make it stop. Blowing can also make moving things change direction.

Science quiz

Daisy is using a straw to blow at a table-tennis ball. Which picture shows her blowing in a way that will make the ball change direction? Circle A or B.

A

B

Science activity

Ask someone to roll or throw a ball towards you. How can you make it change direction? Try different ways.

Which light is the brightest?

Science facts

The Sun is a very bright source of light. You must never look directly at the Sun because the bright light can damage your eyes. Light also comes from other sources, which are not so bright. Candles, torches, room lights and table lamps all give out light.

Science quiz

Which of these candles gives the brightest light? Write **1** in the box by the brightest light; write **2** in the box by the next brightest; and write **3** in the box by the least bright light.

Science activity

(!) Can you find the brightest light in your home? Which one is it?

What makes a shadow?

Science facts

When you shine a torch at a wall, the wall seems brighter. If you put your hand over the torch, it blocks all the light, and the wall stays dark. If you hold your hand between the torch and the wall, you make a shadow. The closer your hand is to the torch, the bigger the shadow.

Science quiz

Which of these children will make the largest shadow? Circle that child's name.

Jo

Kate

Tom

Ben

Science activity

Use a torch and your hands to make a shadow that looks like a bird. Can you make a shadow that looks like a dog?

How do you make that sound?

Science facts

You can make sounds when you beat, shake or scrape things. You can make sounds when you pluck strings or use a bow. Blowing through a hole can also make a sound.

Science quiz

Draw a circle around each instrument that makes a sound when you beat it.

Science activity

Can you make a sound by blowing over the neck of a bottle? What happens when you pour some water into the bottle and then blow over the neck again? How does the sound change?

What makes the loudest sound?

Science facts

You use your ears to hear sounds. Some sounds are loud and easy to hear. Other sounds are quiet and hard to hear. Some sounds are so loud they hurt your ears. People can wear ear protectors to protect their hearing in places where sounds are very loud.

Science quiz

If you stood next to each of these things, which one would sound the loudest? Put a tick (✔) in the box beside it. Which one would sound the quietest? Put a cross (✗) in the box beside it. Circle the one that is so loud you would need to wear ear protectors to stand near it?

Science activity

Can you make sounds with a comb and tissue paper? How can you make the sounds louder?

Contents

Me

Stick a photo of yourself inside the picture frame.

Find and colour the letter that your name begins with.

G L P K

I E M V X

W S J Z O N

C B F Q A

Y U R H D T

All about me

Add more candles to the birthday cake to show your age.

Colour the picture of the boy if you are a boy, and colour the picture of the girl if you are a girl.

Portraits

Draw over the dotted lines and finish the portrait of yourself.

Order the portraits from youngest to oldest. Draw lines to match the pictures to the numbers.

1   2   3   4

My body

Count how many you have. Draw lines to match the pictures to the numbers.

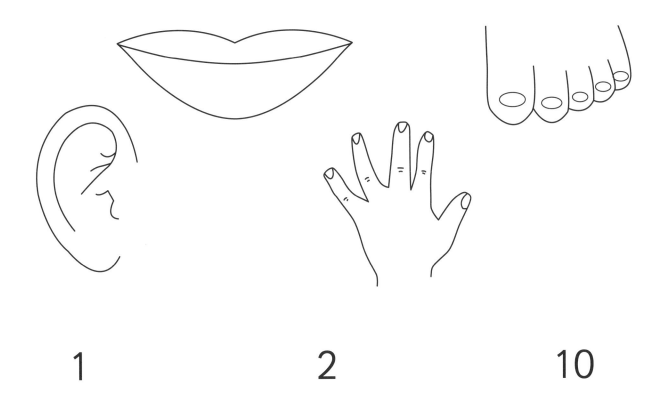

1   2   10

Draw over the dotted lines to show how these people are using their bodies.

My clothes

Draw your favourite clothes in the wardrobe.

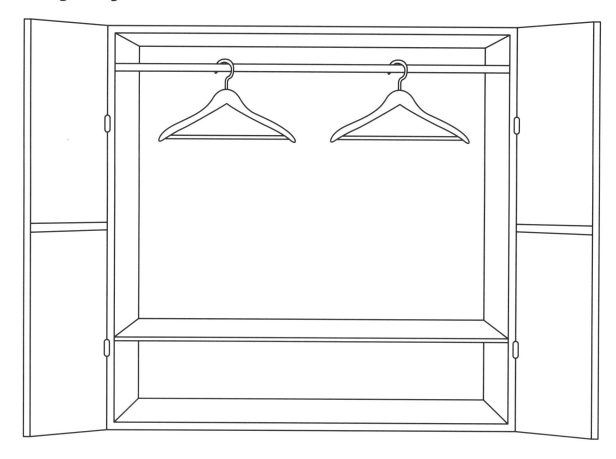

Tell the rainy day story.

Get Set Understanding the World

Fun with clothes

Draw lines to match the clothes to the body parts.

  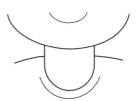 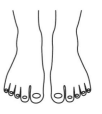

Draw what comes next in each clothes pattern.

My hobbies

Draw a ring around all the hobbies that you like.

Draw your favourite toys in the toy box.

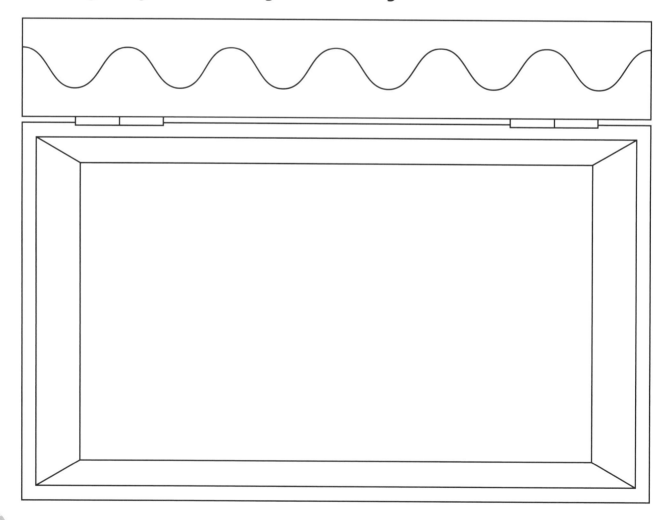

Things to play with

Draw over the wiggly lines to match the objects.

Spot the 5 differences between the dressing-up pictures.
Draw a ring around each one.

My friends

Draw your friends on the bouncy castle.

Colour each friend's clothes a different colour.

12

Being a good friend

Draw a happy or sad face to show whether the children are being good or bad friends.

Draw over the dotted lines to show who is being a good friend. Describe how they are being a good friend.

My family

Draw your family. Count the people and draw a ring around the right number.

1   2   3   4   5   6   7   8   9   10

Talk about the activities that you do with your family. Draw your own activity.

Other families

Talk about how the families are different. Trace the numbers.

2   3   4

Guess which home this family lives in. Explain why.

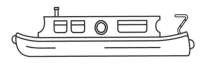

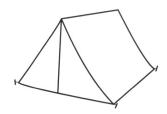

My home

Count the things in your home. Write the numbers in the boxes.

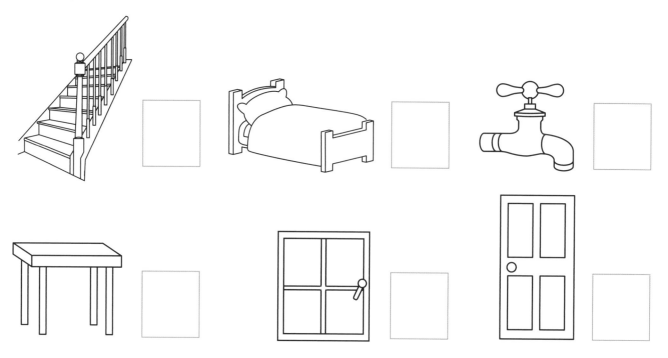

Draw your bedroom.

Get Set Understanding the World

Homes around the world

Draw lines to match the homes to the places.

 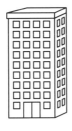  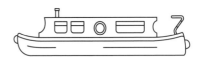

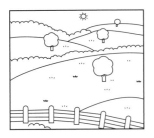   

Colour the castle according to the shapes you can see in it.

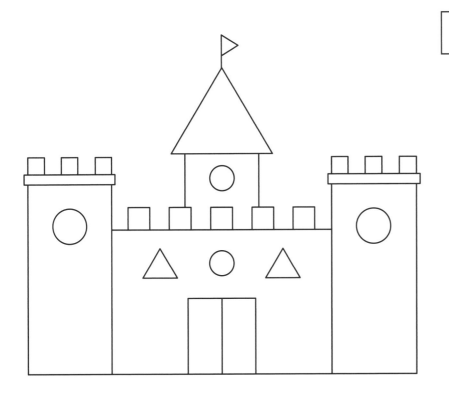

 red

 green

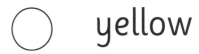 yellow

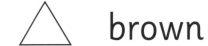 brown

My community

Look outside your window and draw what you can see.

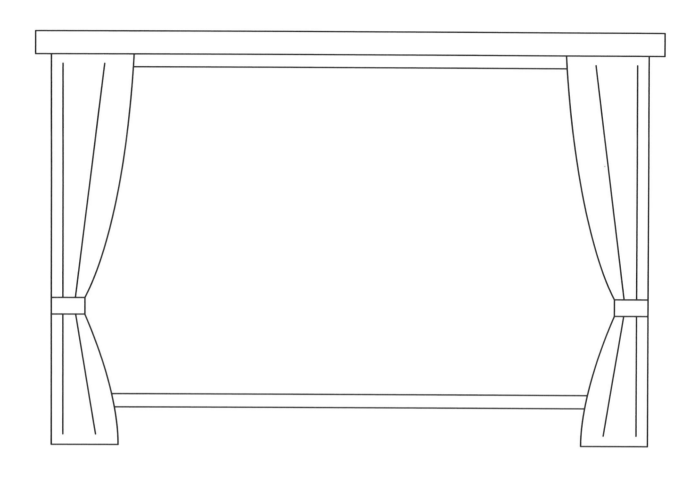

Tick all the places that you go to in your community.

Places in the community

Draw a line through the maze to help the boy get his book back to the library.

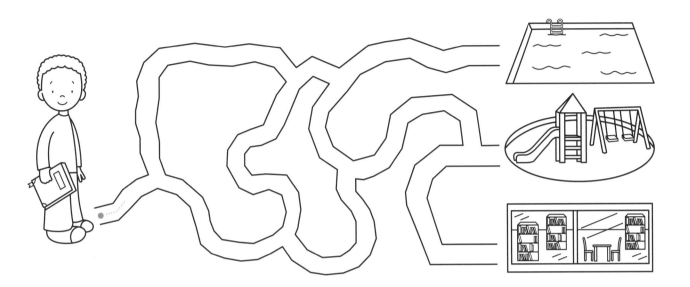

Read the words. Draw the food to help the shopkeeper stack his shelves.

tin   jam   bun   box

People who help us

Describe the people who help us for your adult to guess.

Draw lines to match the people to the places they work.

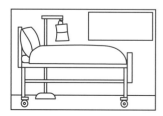 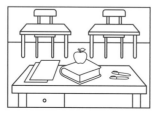  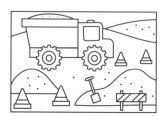

Emergencies

Draw a line on each wiggly road to get to the emergencies on time.

Order the pictures to tell the hospital story. Write a number from 1 to 4 beside each picture.

Being kind to others

Tick all the pictures of people who are being kind.

Draw a picture of a time when you have helped someone.

Religions and beliefs

Colour any objects that are special to your family. Are any of the objects special to your friends' families?

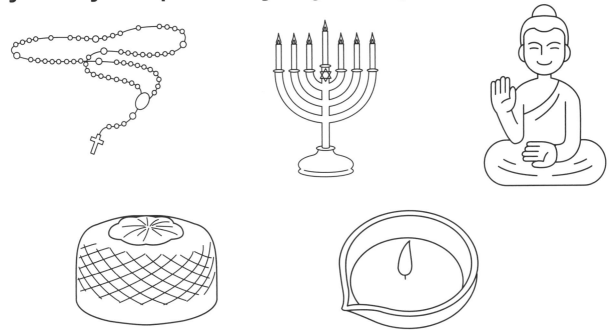

Draw a line on each wiggly road to help the children get to the religious buildings.

Celebrations

Draw lines to match the people to the celebration objects.

Draw a picture of your favourite celebration.

Planning celebrations

Draw or write what you need for a birthday party.

food

drink

fun

Decorate the mask for a fancy dress party.

Foods I like

Find all the foods in the tangle picture. Colour the food that you like the best.

Copy the food names. Draw a ring around the cake and the fruit that you like best.

bun   tart   muffin

plum   lemon   banana

Types of food

Colour the vegetables green and the fruit yellow.

Draw a ring around the odd ones out in each row.

Healthy foods

Draw a ring around all the healthy foods.

Draw a healthy meal on the plate.

Staying healthy

Order the pictures to tell the washing story. Write a number from 1 to 4 beside each picture.

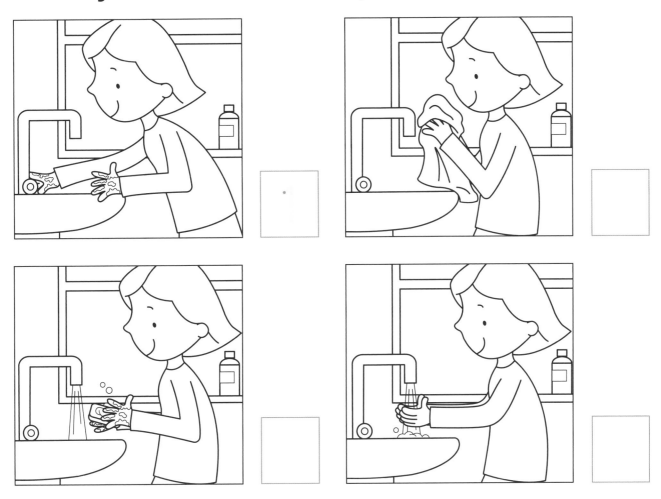

Do each exercise for 20 seconds. Write how many you did.

Notes for parents and carers

Topic	Teaching tip	Key vocabulary	Extension activity
Me page 4	Ask your child to say aloud the *sound* of the letter that their first name begins with.	me, myself, I, you, name, photo	Together, create and decorate a name card for your child's bedroom door.
All about me page 5	Help your child to work out how many candles to draw on the cake by counting on their fingers.	birthday, candle, cake, age, boy, girl	Ask your child to find out their family members' birthdays and mark them on a calendar.
Portraits page 6	Encourage your child to look at all their facial features carefully in the mirror before starting to draw.	head, eye, nose, mouth, baby, child	Show your child a photo of you as a child. Compare how you both look at this age.
My body page 7	Ask your child to point to each body part as they count it.	arm, hand, finger, leg, foot, toe	Make a height chart together to record growth, perhaps in informal units such as hands.
My clothes page 8	Encourage your child to draw a variety of clothes in the wardrobe, including shoes.	trousers, jumper, dress, coat, boot, umbrella	Encourage your child to practise dressing and undressing independently, including putting on socks and doing up buttons and zips.
Fun with clothes page 9	Encourage your child to say aloud the pattern that they can see and what would come next.	T-shirt, shorts, skirt, sock, glove, scarf	With your child, make your own real clothes patterns. Socks are great for this!
My hobbies page 10	Ask your child to say why they like or dislike each hobby or toy.	hobby, toy, play, favourite, like, dislike	With your child, try a new hobby together. Discuss what they liked or disliked about it.
Things to play with page 11	Check that your child is holding the pencil correctly. Encourage them to move their pencil slowly and carefully along the wiggly lines.	sport, music, football, painting, reading, dressing up	With your child, make a sock puppet to play with.
My friends page 12	Ask your child why the children they are drawing on the bouncy castle are their friends. What makes them a good friend?	friend, friendship, together, share, care, feelings	Help your child to make a friendship card for one of their friends.
Being a good friend page 13	Ask your child why the children in the picture are not being good friends and how they could change their behaviour.	happy, sad, angry, upset, thank you, sorry	Make a friendship flower together from coloured paper. Show different ways of being a good friend on each petal.
My family page 14	To represent each member of your family, gather dolls or teddy bears together and count them.	family, parent, mum, dad, brother, sister	Create a family photo album together, with photos of extended family members.
Other families page 15	Encourage your child to trace the numbers as accurately as they can, with the pencil flowing. Help with posture and pencil grip.	only child, twin, stepmother, stepfather, grandparent, pet	Ask your child to use small-world toys or play dough to build different kinds of families. Talk about what they have made.
My home page 16	Help your child to use a tally chart to keep count of the objects around your home.	home, room, bedroom, door, window, stairs	Ask your child to design their ideal bedroom.
Homes around the world page 17	Encourage your child to find and name the shapes. You may need to help them understand the key.	house, flat, cottage, houseboat, hut, castle	Read *Wonderful Houses Around the World* by Yoshio Komatsu.

Get Set Understanding the World

Topic	Teaching tip	Key vocabulary	Extension activity
My community page 18	Talk together about why you go to each place in your community and who you see there.	town, country, community, local, building, area	Walk around your local community together and talk about all the places you see.
Places in the community page 19	Help your child to decode the food words by sounding out each letter using the phonics sounds that they know.	library, swimming pool, park, playground, shop, school	Visit a library with your child, choose a special book and read it together.
People who help us page 20	Encourage your child to describe what the person does in their job, as well as their clothes and the objects they are holding.	job, work, uniform, police officer, firefighter, chef	Encourage your child to play dressing up, trying on outfits and uniforms for different jobs. Talk about the jobs.
Emergencies page 21	Prompt your child to describe what is happening in each story picture. Then ask them to tell you the whole story.	fire engine, ambulance, police car, emergency, doctor, hospital	Take turns pretending to be a police officer and a criminal, using paint to take fingerprints.
Being kind to others page 22	Ask your child to consider the finer details when drawing. For example, "Are legs and arms really as thin as a stick?".	kind, help, fight, shout, right, wrong	Encourage your child to do something kind for a friend or family member.
Religions and beliefs page 23	Help your child to understand that different people have different beliefs and that we are all part of a diverse society.	religion, place of worship, church, synagogue, mosque, temple	With your child, choose a religion to find out more about and read a child-friendly religious story together.
Celebrations page 24	Encourage your child to think about the celebration, who was there, what food they ate and any traditions that are part of it.	Halloween, Eid, Chinese New Year, Christmas, Diwali, Hanukkah	Use paints to create a firework picture together.
Planning celebrations page 25	Ask your child to say and show on their fingers how many sounds they can hear in a word before writing it.	party, game, fancy dress, mask, card, gift	Wrap some gifts for a party using different 3D objects – cubes, cuboids and cylinders. Write a label for each present.
Foods I like page 26	Help your child form the letters, starting from the right place and moving in the right direction.	ice cream, strawberry, tomato, pizza, broccoli, taste	Role-play a restaurant, taking it in turns to play the waiter and the customer, and ordering food that you like.
Types of food page 27	Encourage your child to suggest which foods are healthy or unhealthy and why.	eat, fruit, vegetable, meat, fish, dairy	With your child, look in the fridge and sort the food into different food groups.
Healthy foods page 28	Help your child to include different food groups in the healthy meal so it is balanced.	healthy, unhealthy, sugar, fats, sweet, savoury	With your child, plan and create a packed lunch or picnic with healthy foods.
Staying healthy page 29	Encourage your child to do the exercises as quickly as they can, so they can feel the impact on their bodies.	clean, exercise, run, jump, stretch, body	Ask your child to make a washing-hands poster to place by the sink.

Schofield&Sims

Help children to become school-ready with **Get Set Early Years**, an engaging cross-curricular programme to bridge the gap between play and formal learning.

Developed by experienced practitioners and based on the Early Years Foundation Stage framework, **Get Set Early Years** is designed to build confidence, encourage curiosity and foster a love of learning.

- exciting and motivating activities to support classroom teaching
- friendly illustrations that children can enjoy colouring in
- key vocabulary for each topic area, providing opportunities to create a rich language environment
- notes and tips for parents and carers to help you delve further into each topic

Get Set Understanding the World: People invites children to explore the differences between themselves and others, developing their understanding of the world as a diverse place full of different people and traditions. This book covers topics such as clothes, hobbies, friends, families and communities.

Discover the other **Get Set** activity books:

ISBN 978-07217-1447-9

9 780721 714479

MIX
Paper from responsible sources
FSC® C023114

ISBN 978 07217 1447 9
Early Years
Age range 4–5 years
£3.95 (Retail price)

For further information and to place your order visit
www.schofieldandsims.co.uk or telephone 01484 607080